Andrew Lloyd Webber

presents

A R Rahman's
BOMBAY DREAMS

Lyrics by Don Black

Vocal Selections

A Really Useful Group Publication

Production photos by Alastair Muir.
Additional photos by Hugo Glendenning.
Music arranged by Jack Long.
Music processed by Paul Ewers Music Design.
Cover artwork by Dewynters plc.
Printed and bound in Great Britain.

World premiere at The Apollo Victoria Theatre 19th June 2002.

Order No. RG10384
ISBN 0-7119-9641-5

Exclusive Distributors:
Music Sales Limited, 8/9 Frith Street, London W1D 3JB, England.
Music Sales Pty Limited, 120 Rothschild Avenue, Rosebery, NSW 2018, Australia.

www.musicsales.com

'Shakalaka Baby' by A R Rahman, Don Black & Marius De Vries.
'Chaiyya Chaiyya' Music by A R Rahman, Lyrics by Gulzar.

Bombay Dreams

Music by A R Rahman
Lyrics by Don Black

Sun - rise, burn - ing heat; no - thing is as tra - velled as a Bom - bay street.

Con - tra - dic - tions, ci - ty of ex - tremes, a - ny - thing is pos - si - ble in Bom - bay Dreams.

ding a ding_ a da   di gi di gi da da ding a ding_ a da   di gi di gi da da

ding a ding_ a da   di gi di gi da   da ding a ding_ a da.

EUNUCHS

SWEETIE

We eu - nuchs bring you luck,   give us mo - ney you will see.   I can change your for - tune

if you are kind to me. But if you re-fuse us you'll face ad-ver-si-ty,

ev-en though we're not the men we used_ to be!

PRIYA

1. Life's nev-er ea-sy,_____ ev-'ry day you strug-gle through._
2. Life's nev-er ea-sy,_____ ev-'ry day's an up-hill fight._

1.

You lean on me,_ I lean on you.
Pray'rs are ig-nored,

Love's Never Easy

Music by A R Rahman
Lyrics by Don Black

We have seen life through men's eyes,__ so we know__ what plea - ses you.__

Oh._____

Oh._____ Oh._____

Oh._____

Love's nev-er ea-sy,_____ you will learn this les-son too._____
Love's nev-er ea-sy,_____ take it from a girl who knows.____

_____ I'll be__ here for you when you do. }
_____ Love comes as quick-ly as it goes. }

Love's nev-er ea-sy,_____ one day soon the dream will start.

Well, that__ is what I tell my heart.

Love's nev - er ea - sy.

Shakalaka Baby

Music & Lyrics by
A R Rahman, Don Black & Marius De Vries

come and Sha - ka - la - ka with me. Sha - ka - la - ka Ba - by,

Sha - ka - la - ka Ba - by, no - thing here is ev - er what it seems.

Sha - ka - la - ka Ba - by, Sha - ka - la - ka Ba - by, let me take you with me in my

dreams. (No no no no no no no no___ no no no no no no no no

1. B⁷
no no no___ no no.

2. Am
A se-cret moon and a

Bm
jas - mine breeze:

Am
pray we'll share ma - ny nights like these,

Bm
a mil - lion stars in the

C

B⁵
sky._____

N.C.
(Oh, oh, oh, oh.)

Em
Sha - ka - la - ka Ba - by, Sha - ka - la - ka Ba - by.

B⁵

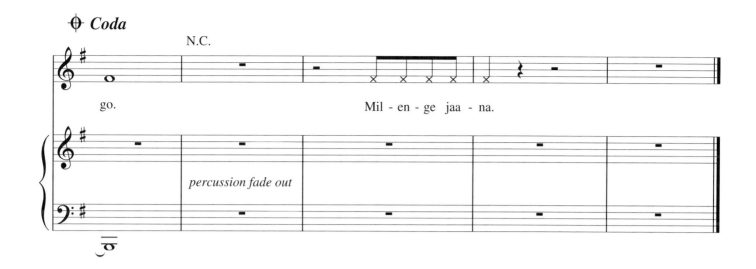

$\oplus$ *Coda*

go.

Mil - en - ge jaa - na.

percussion fade out

Verse 2:
In a trance, going out of my mind
You made a flame that keeps me burning
Come on, baby, give me a sign
One word from you and the world stops turning
(Oh, oh, oh) Music is inside me
(Oh, oh, oh, oh) I need you here beside me
(Oh, oh) I know you'll satisfy me
That you are my Bombay lover.
Shakalaka baby, shakalaka baby
This is how it's really meant to be
Shakalaka baby, shakalaka baby
Come and shakalaka with me.
Shakalaka baby, shakalaka baby
I just wanna love you every day
Shakalaka baby, shakalaka baby
Promise me you'll never go away.

Verse 4:
Shakalaka baby, shakalaka baby
This is how it's really meant to be
Shakalaka baby, shakalaka baby
Come and shakalaka with me.
Shakalaka baby, shakalaka baby
Nothing here at all I need to know
Shakalaka baby, shakalaka baby
Now you're here, I'll never let you go.

Chaiyya Chaiyya

Music by A R Rahman
Lyrics by Gulzar

chaiy - ya chaiy - ya chaiy - ya chaiy - ya. Chal - le   chaiy - ya   chaiy - ya chaiy - ya   chaiy - ya. Chal - le

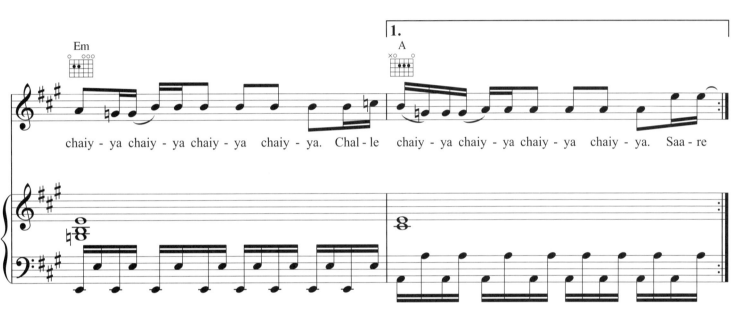

chaiy - ya chaiy - ya chaiy - ya   chaiy - ya. Chal - le   chaiy - ya chaiy - ya chaiy - ya   chaiy - ya. Saa - re

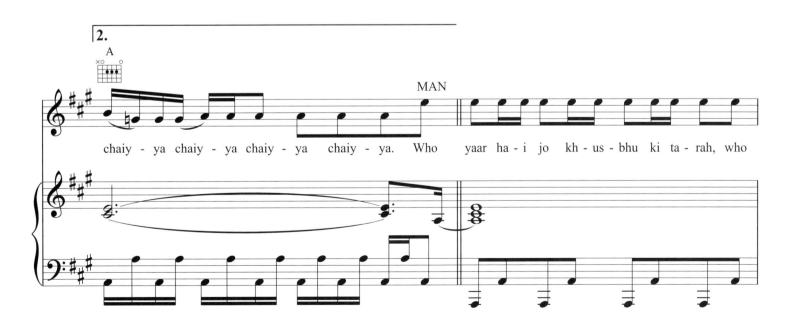

chaiy - ya chaiy - ya chaiy - ya   chaiy - ya. Who   yaar ha - i jo kh - us - bhu ki ta - rah, who

MAN

Gul-po-sh kab-hi it-raye ka-hin meh_ ke to naz-ar___ aa___ ja-ye ka-hin._____

33

WOMAN

Taa -

po - sh kab - hi it - ra - ye___ ka - hin meh - ke to na - zaar aa___ jaye ka - hin.

- be - ez ban - aa ke pah - noo us - e aa___ y at ki ta - rah mil___ jaaye ka - hin.

Me - ra

Me - ra

Nag - ma wa - hi me - ra kal - ma wa - hi me - ra nag - ma nag - ma me - ra kal - ma kal - ma me - ra

chaiy - ya chaiy - ya chaiy - ya chaiy - ya. Chal - le   chaiy - ya chaiy - ya chaiy - ya chaiy - ya. Chal - le

chaiy - ya chaiy - ya chaiy - ya chaiy - ya. Chal - le   chaiy - ya chaiy - ya chaiy - ya chaiy - ya. Chal - le

chaiy - ya chaiy - ya chaiy - ya chaiy - ya. Chal - le   chaiy - ya chaiy - ya chaiy - ya chaiy - ya chal - le

chaiy - ya chaiy - ya chaiy - ya chaiy - ya.

N.C. (open A)

Only Love

Music by A R Rahman
Lyrics by Don Black

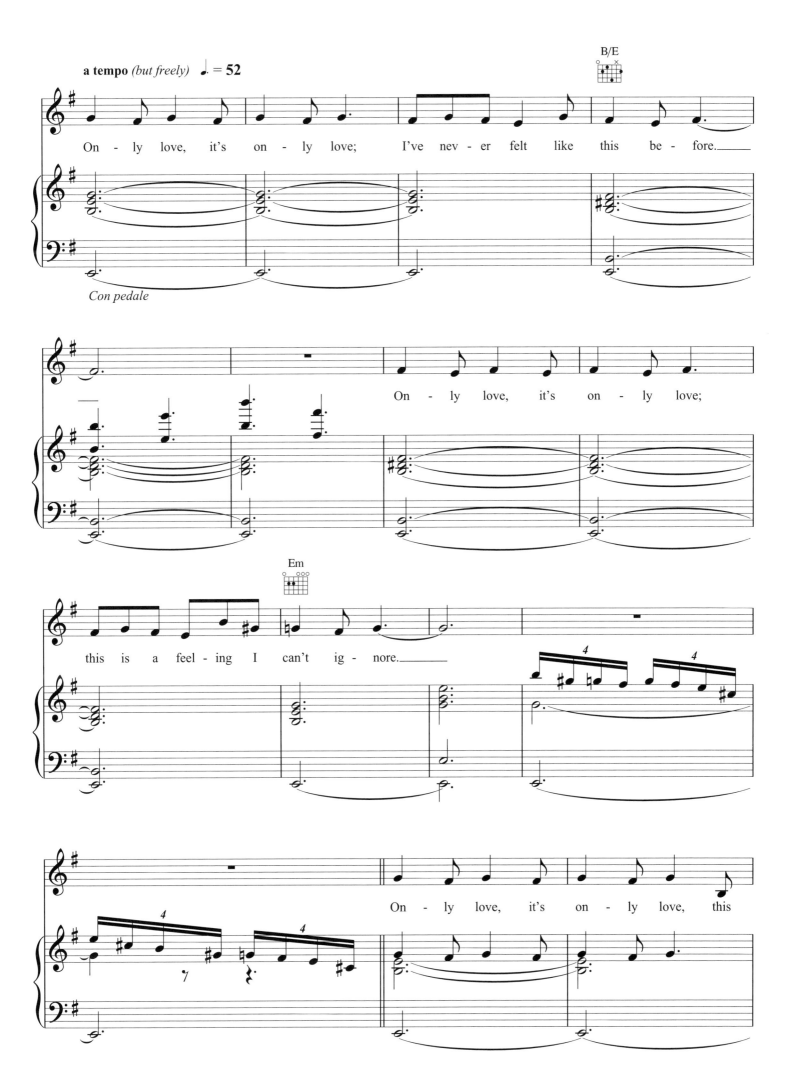

music that's play - ing in - side my head._____ On - ly love, I

know it's love with - out a word ev - er be - ing said._____

Some - thing strange has hap - pened here, I'm no long - er free._____

I can't get you off my mind;___ what is wrong with me?_____

How Many Stars?

Music by A R Rahman
Lyrics by Don Black

that pre-cious gifts can come from emp-ty__ hands.

PRIYA

Pre-cious gifts can come from emp-ty__ hands.

AKAASH

How ma-ny

PRIYA

How ma-ny

stars__ have to shine be-fore we find our way? How ma-ny

Closer Than Ever

Music by A R Rahman
Lyrics by Don Black

Lyrics:
There'll come a morn - ing when we'll a - wak - en clos - er than ev - er;

slow - ly but sure - ly, soon - er or lat - er, clos - er than ev - er;

breath - ing the same_ air, dream - ing the same_ dreams, clos - er then ev - er_____

_____ be - fore.

PRIYA
There'll come a mo - ment when I will hold_ you clos - er than ev - er._____

AKAASH
There'll come a mo - ment when I will hold_ you clos - er than ev - er._____

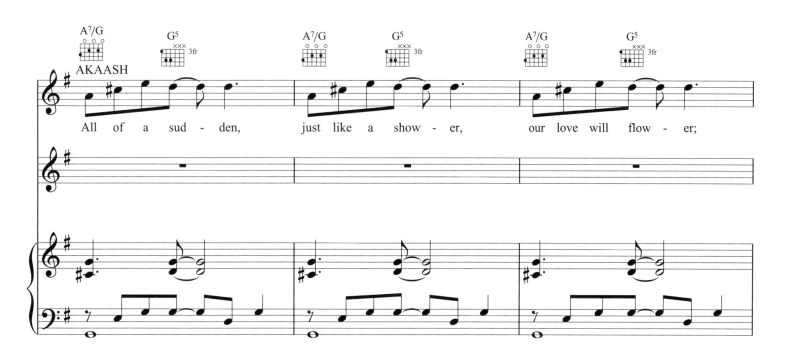

AKAASH

All of a sud - den,   just like a show - er,   our love will flow - er;

The Journey Home

Music by A R Rahman
Lyrics by Don Black

jour - ney home_____ is nev - er too long;_____ your
(Verse 2 see block lyric)

when my pil - low was___ a ship___ I sailed_____ through the night.

make.

ad lib. vocal

Verse 2:
The journey home is never too long
When open arms are waiting there
The journey home is never too long
There's room to love and room to spare
I want to feel the way that I did then
I'll think my wishes through before
I wish again.